# YOU'RE SOME[THING ELSE,] SNOOPY!

### by Charles M. Schulz

Selected Cartoons from
*The Unsinkable Charlie Brown*, Vol. 2

A FAWCETT CREST BOOK

Fawcett Publications, Inc., Greenwich, Conn.

YOU'RE SOMETHING SPECIAL, SNOOPY!

This book, prepared especially for Fawcett Publications, Inc.,
comprises the second half of *THE UNSINKABLE CHARLIE
BROWN,* and is reprinted by arrangement with Holt, Rinehart
& Winston, Inc.

Printed in the United States of America
July 1972

I REFUSE TO CHASE A STICK THAT HASN'T BEEN PROPERLY SANDED AND POLISHED!

COME BACK HERE WITH THAT SHOE, YOU STUPID DOG!!!

LOOK AT THIS...I'M WALKING AROUND WITH ONLY ONE SHOE! I CAN'T GO AROUND LIKE THIS...I'LL WEAR OUT MY SOCK!

WHAT ARE YOU GOING TO DO ABOUT IT?

WELL?

TICKLE! TICKLE! TICKLE!

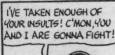

C'MON, FORGET ABOUT EATING! FIGHT LIKE A MAN!

NO! I'M NOT GONNA SHAKE HANDS!

IF YOU WANT TO GET OUT OF THIS FIGHT, YOU'RE GOING TO HAVE TO APOLOGIZE BY KISSING MY HAND!

*SIGH*

I ACCEPT YOUR APOLOGY!

SMACK!

WHAT'S A LITTLE PRIDE WHERE YOUR STOMACH IS CONCERNED?

SCHULZ

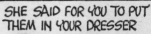

LOOK, THE FIRST OFFICIAL LEAF OF AUTUMN!

LEAVES HAVE BEEN FALLING FOR WEEKS... WHAT MAKES THAT ONE SO OFFICIAL?

I HAD IT NOTARIZED!

CHARLIE BROWN-N-N! IT'S THAT TIME OF YEAR AGAIN!

TUM TE DUM TE TA DE DUM ♩

I'LL HOLD THE BALL, CHARLIE BROWN, AND YOU COME RUNNING UP, AND KICK IT...OKAY?

OKAY!

SHE THINKS I'M STUPID... SHE PLANS TO PULL THE BALL AWAY WHEN I COME RUNNING UP TO KICK IT, BUT THIS YEAR I'M GOING TO FOOL HER!

THIS YEAR I'M JUST GOING TO MAKE HER WAIT! IF I HAVE TO, I'LL SIT HERE IN THE HOUSE UNTIL MIDNIGHT, AND MAKE HER WAIT!

WELL, I'LL BE! SHE'S SOUND ASLEEP!

THIS IS MY BIG CHANCE...

SHE REALLY SLIPPED UP THIS TIME!

AAUGH!

WHAM!

WE FANATICS ARE LIGHT SLEEPERS, CHARLIE BROWN!

NOW, ALL YOU HAVE TO DO IS HOLD THE KITE LIKE THIS, AND THEN LET GO WHEN I TELL YOU TO...

ARE YOU READY?

FANTASTIC!

HAVE YOU EVER KNOWN ANYONE WHO HAS THE GIFT OF PROPHECY?

JUST MYSELF

YOU?!

ABSOLUTELY! I CAN PREDICT WHAT ANY ADULT WILL ANSWER WHEN HE OR SHE IS ASKED A CERTAIN QUESTION..

IF YOU GO UP TO AN ADULT, AND SAY, "HOW COME WE HAVE A MOTHER'S DAY AND A FATHER'S DAY, BUT WE DON'T HAVE A CHILDREN'S DAY?" THAT ADULT WILL ALWAYS ANSWER, "EVERY DAY IS CHILDREN'S DAY!"

IT DOESN'T MATTER WHAT ADULT YOU ASK... YOU WILL ALWAYS GET THE SAME ANSWER...IT IS AN ABSOLUTE CERTAINTY!

I'LL TRY IT OUT ON GRANDMA..

GRANDMA, HOW COME WE HAVE A MOTHER'S DAY AND A FATHER'S DAY, BUT WE DON'T HAVE A CHILDREN'S DAY?

EVERY DAY IS CHILDREN'S DAY

THE GIFT OF PROPHECY!

I'VE TOLD YOU A MILLION TIMES THAT ADULTS ARE DIFFERENT!

YOU HAVE TO BE ABLE TO READ THEM..

YOU KNOW WHAT YOUR TROUBLE IS? YOU JUST DON'T UNDERSTAND THE ADULT MIND..

I CAN PREDICT WHAT THE AVERAGE ADULT WILL SAY OR DO IN ALMOST ANY GIVEN SITUATION...

THIS IS A MUST IF YOU ARE GOING TO SURVIVE AS A CHILD!

NOW, TAKE GRANDMA, FOR INSTANCE...I CAN PREDICT EXACTLY WHAT SHE WILL SAY IN THE FOLLOWING SITUATION....

YOU DRAW A PICTURE AND I'LL DRAW A PICTURE...THEN YOU TAKE THE TWO PICTURES IN, AND SHOW THEM TO GRANDMA...

ASK HER WHICH PICTURE SHE THINKS IS THE BETTER..I PREDICT THAT SHE WILL LOOK AT THEM AND SAY,"WHY, I THINK THEY'RE BOTH VERY NICE"

GRANDMA, HERE ARE TWO PICTURES THAT LINUS AND I HAVE DRAWN...WHICH ONE DO YOU THINK IS THE BETTER?

WHY, I THINK THEY'RE BOTH VERY NICE

YOU JUST HAVE TO UNDERSTAND THE ADULT MIND!

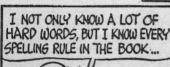

YES, MA'AM? ME? WHY DID I HAVE MY HEAD ON MY DESK? YOU DON'T KNOW? YOU'RE ASKING ME WHY I HAD MY HEAD ON MY DESK?

BECAUSE I BLEW THE STUPID SPELLING BEE, THAT'S WHY!!!

OH, GOOD GRIEF! NOW, I'VE DONE IT!

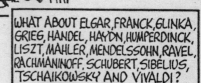

YOU KNOW WHAT?

WHAT?

A PEANUT BUTTER SANDWICH IS JUST THE SANDWICH TO BE EATING WHEN YOU'RE LOOKING ACROSS THE PLAYGROUND AT A LITTLE RED-HAIRED GIRL YOU ADMIRE, BUT KNOW YOU HAVEN'T A CHANCE OF EVER MEETING

WHY IS THAT?

IF YOU HAVE TO ASK, YOU'LL NEVER UNDERSTAND!

HELLO, SCHROEDER? GUESS WHAT... I CALLED TO TELL YOU I'VE BEEN LISTENING TO SOME BEETHOVEN MUSIC

I'VE ALSO BEEN READING HIS BIOGRAPHY...IT'S VERY INTERESTING. SORT OF SAD, AND YET SORT OF INSPIRING...YOU KNOW WHAT I MEAN?

I HAVE A POST CARD, TOO, THAT I THINK YOU'D LIKE ... AN UNCLE OF MINE SENT IT TO ME FROM BONN, GERMANY...THEY HAVE A MUSEUM THERE

I GUESS THAT'S WHERE BEETHOVEN WAS BORN, ISN'T IT? I'LL BET YOU'D ENJOY VISITING THERE.. MAYBE YOU'LL HAVE A CHANCE TO SOMEDAY...

ANYWAY, THAT'S WHY I CALLED BECAUSE I KNEW YOU'D BE INTERESTED, AND I JUST WANTED TO TELL YOU ABOUT THESE THINGS...

IT'S NOT PROPER FOR A GIRL TO CALL A BOY ON THE TELEPHONE

AAUGH!!

SCHULZ

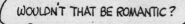

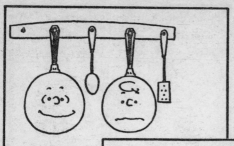

IF DECEMBER TWELFTH IS HERE, CAN BEETHOVEN'S BIRTHDAY BE FAR AWAY?

GUESS WHAT...BEETHOVEN'S BIRTHDAY IS THIS WEEK, ISN'T IT? WELL, I'M GOING TO BAKE A CAKE, AND HAVE EVERYONE OVER! HOW ABOUT THAT?

I THINK SUCH AN EFFORT ON MY PART DESERVES A REWARD, DON'T YOU? LIKE MAYBE A LITTLE KISS...

I MEAN, AFTER ALL, SOMEONE LIKE YOURSELF WHO ADMIRES BEETHOVEN SO MUCH SHOULD BE WILLING TO REWARD A PERSON WHO WORKS HARD TO...

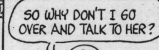

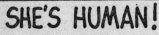

HEY! ZIP!

WHAT DO YOU THINK YOU'RE DOING?

NO FUTURE HUSBAND OF MINE IS GOING TO SIT AROUND HOLDING A BLANKET!

I'M NOT YOUR FUTURE HUSBAND GIVE ME THAT BLANKET!

NO!

I LOOK FORWARD TO THE DAY WHEN I'LL UNDERSTAND GIRLS..

WHO'S GONNA SLUG WHO? / WHAT? / GO AHEAD, **BIG** BROTHER...SLUG HIM A GOOD ONE!

ALL RIGHT, CHARLIE BROWN, I'VE HEARD ENOUGH! C'MON, PUT 'EM UP! PUT 'EM UP, AND LET'S GET THIS OVER RIGHT NOW! C'MON, PUT 'EM UP!

BLEAH!

RE'S THE WORLD WAR I LOT DOWN BEHIND EMY LINES...WHAT'S IS? IT LOOKS LIKE SKIRMISH! PROBABLY O SQUADS OF INFANTRY..

CHARGE!

I NEVER KNOW WHAT'S GOING ON..

Schulz